Cats

with Vimrod

cats

having nine lives
can sometimes be
quite
tiring.

i think i'll
take a nap.

Vimrd by Lisa Swerling and Ralph Lazar

HarperCollins*Publishers*

i would like to be a `cat`
for a day so i could sleep
at my desk without

`major repercussions`

immortality

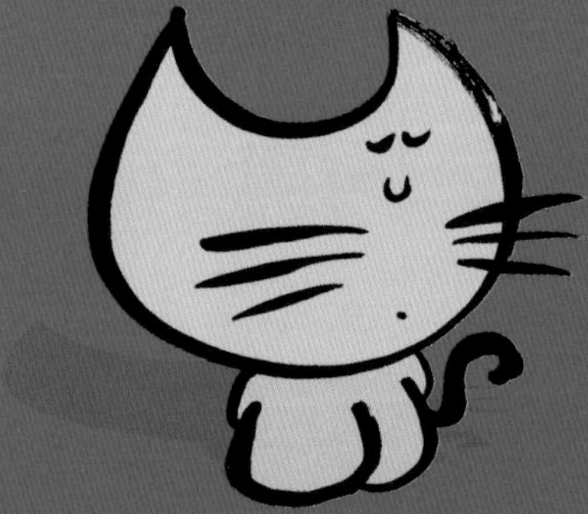

is

over-
rated

we can move our ears
independently of
one another.

can you?

no, you can't.
respect.
thank you.

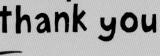

i reckon god doesn't give a toss when we kill pigeons

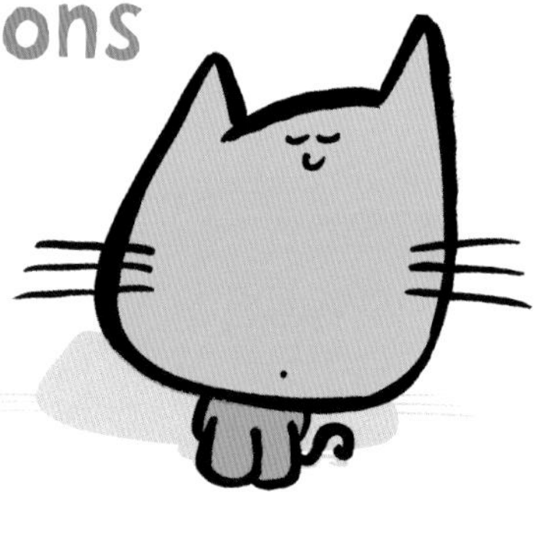

i have called my cat

rover

(primarily
to confuse
my in-laws)

yes, her name is

cleopatra

and yes,
she bathes
in milk, and
no, she is
not spoilt.

purr

i've been so busy doing nothing recently that i think i'm going to lie down and rest

just because you have the ability to completely turn off to the sound of my voice, doesn't necessarily mean you are superior. i said, just because you have the ability to completely turn off to the sound of my voice, doesn't necessarily mean you are superior

shut up and
pamper me

sunrise, sunset,
sunrise, sunset
etc

the waves of

lap upon

the beach of

destiny,

but i couldn't be
bothered quite
frankly because
i am a

i can't make it to the
meeting because my
head is caught
in the
cat
flap.
don't
ask,
just
don't
ask.

49%
pussycat

51%
total
bitch

i'm bored...
...think i might
go and
instigate an
altercation.

bad
whisker
day

i actually
can't imagine
how hideous
it must be
to be a dog

i have had a most
excellent morning
given that it was
only 10 minutes long.

i strongly
recommend
sleeping until
11h50.

lisa swerling + ralph lazar

are two of the uk's most popular
graphic artists. through their company
last lemon they have brought to life a
range of inspired cartoon characters,
including harold's planet, the brainwaves,
blessthischick and, of course, vimrod.

they are married with two children,
and live in london.

HarperCollins*Publishers*
77–85 Fulham Palace Road, Hammersmith, London W6 8JB

www.harpercollins.co.uk

Published by HarperCollins*Publishers* 2008
1

A catalogue record for this book is available from the British Library
ISBN-10 0-00-728031-5
ISBN-13 978-0-00-728031-5

Set in Bokka
Printed and bound in China by Leo Paper Products

other titles in the collection:

drink!
Wine is made to be drunk,
i am drunk,
therefore
am i wine?

shopping
it's the little voices that tell me to go shopping

farting
my farts hospitalise small children

xmas
christmas is coming run!

dads
life is a journey between the fridge and the sofa

chocolate
life is a struggle between good, evil and chocolate

love
You and me... and two hamsters on the spinning-wheel of life

mums
behind every great woman is her bum

life
life is terribly long isn't it? shall we rest?

insults
the way you breathe really irritates me

indulgence
girls like us deserve the best. plus a little extra

blokehood
beer is the oil that greases the engine of the soul

dogs
the answer to the universe is woof.

(watch this space)

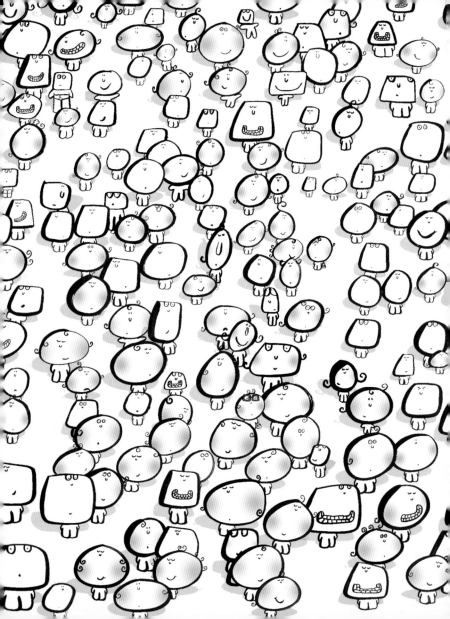